THE
LIFE
AND
MINISTRY
OF
JESUS
CHRIST

The Life & Ministry of Jesus Christ

BOOK II

From the Sermon on the Mount to His Last Journey to Jerusalem

NAVPRESS

A MINISTRY OF THE NAVIGATORS

©1977 by The Navigators
All rights reserved including translation
ISBN 0-89109-021-5
Fifth Printing, 1979

The Navigators is an international, evangelical Christian organization. Jesus
Christ gave His followers the Great Commission to go and make disciples
(Matthew 28:19). The aim of The Navigators is to help fulfill that commission by
multiplying laborers for Christ in every nation.

Printed in the United States of America

The drawing on the front cover is that of a fisherman's net, symbolizing the
middle part of Jesus' ministry when He was training His disciples to become
fishers of men (Matthew 4:19).

CONTENTS

LUKE in his introduction to the Book of Acts, said, "In my former book . . . I wrote about all that Jesus began to do and to teach until the day He was taken up to heaven" (Acts 1:1-2). This three-book study, *The Life and Ministry of Jesus Christ,* is designed to help the involved Christian investigate for himself what Jesus did and taught.

The study is primarily for the Christian who has at least one to two years' experience doing personal Bible study and wants to learn more about Jesus Christ. It particularly emphasizes applying biblical truth to one's own life. Anyone who faithfully completes this study should not only have a working knowledge of the life and ministry of Jesus, but a realization that in the process his own life has been changed to become more like Christ's.

This study is based on A. T. Robertson's *A Harmony of the Gospels* (Harper & Brothers, 1950). A harmony arranges the four gospel accounts of the life of Jesus in parallel form in order to provide one continuous narrative of His life and ministry. Some events, such as the feeding of the 5,000, are recorded in all four gospels; others appear in only one, such as Jesus' interview with Nicodemus in the Gospel of John. Mark's gospel is the most chronological; the other three, particularly Matthew's, are topical and follow a theme rather than a chronology. For example, an incident in Matthew 10 might have taken place before one recorded in Matthew 5 (see the chart on pages 82-85).

Another reason for seeming chronological discrepancies in the gospels is that Jesus taught the same truths, told the same parables, and performed similar miracles many times in his three-and-a-half-year ministry. So Matthew recorded the contents of the Sermon on the Mount in one large section toward the beginning of Jesus' ministry (Matthew 5—7), while Luke wrote down similar teachings of Jesus throughout His ministry (Luke 6:17-49; 11:1-13; 13:22-30). Undoubtedly Jesus pronounced woes (judgment) on those who opposed and harassed Him a number of times, so Matthew tells of an incident in Galilee toward the middle of His ministry (Matthew 12:22-45) while Luke records another such confrontation, this time in Judea, later in His ministry (Luke 11:14-36). These are not contradictions but records of similar events.

In a Bible study of this type and size, it is impossible to include every incident in the life and ministry of Jesus that is recorded in the gospels. So only the major events have been included, yet the entire study discusses and accounts for all the passages in the four gospels. The chart at the end of the book lists the passages and the order in which you will study them according to the arrangement in Robertson's harmony.

One of the lasting benefits of this study is that when you have finished all three books, you have, in a sense, written your own commentary on the life and ministry of Jesus Christ. This book, with the other two, will serve as a ready reference to the life of Jesus any time you need it. Through your own diligent study you will have done what Bible scholars and commentators do—researched, thought through, and applied the biblical text. In effect, your bookshelf now will hold your own exposition of the life and ministry of Jesus Christ.

Each book of the series has six chapters, and these may be studied in six discussion sessions, or 12 or more sessions if you prefer a slower pace. The suggested procedure is for you to study the assigned portion—a chapter, half a chapter, or a certain number of questions—and write out all the answers, including the applications. Then, as you meet with your Bible study group or class, you should discuss with others what you have discovered and applied. From the discussion write out any additional remarks or observations in the *Personal Notes* columns. This will maximize your understanding, appreciation, and application of the biblical text.

Book II traces the life and ministry of Jesus from the Sermon on the Mount to the beginning of His last journey to Jerusalem. The six chapters of this book focus on the middle years of Jesus' ministry—His continued popularity with the crowds, the intensifying opposition of the religious leaders, the training of His disciples in light of the opposition. The major emphasis of this period is on His intensive training of His faithful followers for the task that would soon be theirs.

You will find that this segment of the life of Jesus contains numerous lessons for your life and ministry today. You will also discover many applications which you can begin putting into practice in your own situation. This section clearly shows Jesus as the One who has the words of eternal life (John 6:68).

TIME and prayer are the important means for you to get the most out of this study on the life and ministry of Jesus Christ. You must prepare carefully and undergird your study with prayer. Each chapter should be completed in about three to five hours, if you plan to discuss a whole chapter per session. You should set your own pace ahead of time. That can be from half a chapter per discussion session (requiring one-and-a-half to two-and-a-half hours preparation time) to a maximum of an entire chapter per session. Most chapters allow flexibility in terms of depth; you can spend as many or as few hours in preparation, study, and discussion as your schedule allows. Naturally, the person who goes beyond immediate answers, develops his own questions, and uses the *Personal Notes* columns (see that section in these instructions) will benefit most.

Depending on your own study habits, you may keep the books in their original binders, or cut the pages out carefully and place them in a loose-leaf notebook so that you can add other pages and research material later.

Reference Materials

Scripture itself—the four gospels and some verses in Acts 1—is what you will be studying. But because not all the information called for in this study will be found in the Bible, additional reference materials will be helpful. Some suggested ones are:
1. A reliable Bible dictionary and/or encyclopedia.
2. An up-to-date Bible atlas.
3. A good Bible handbook.
4. A simple, English-text commentary.
5. An exhaustive concordance.
6. A harmony of the gospels.

Some of the above are mentioned and referred to in the footnotes and in the bibliography (page 80). (No specific recommendations are made for books in the above list [except for atlases—see under *Maps* in these instructions] because of the many theological positions represented in them. Ask your group leader, pastor, or teacher for recommendations.)

Questions and Charts

The questions and charts in this study are designed to provide factual information as well as to encourage you to dig deeper for the reasons behind certain actions and words of Jesus. You will need some initiative and creativity of thought in answering some of the "why" and "how" questions and in filling in some of the charts. Not all of the blanks in some charts must necessarily be filled in. In addition, opinion questions are included, which do not necessarily have "right" or "wrong" answers, but lend themselves well to a stimulating discussion.

Each section in this study includes a reference or a series of references from the gospels. The ones in **boldface** are the ones you should study, for the questions in that section will be based on those passages. The other references are parallel passages which may be studied if you so desire. You should read the assigned Scriptures in at least two different versions. An example of the format is:

MATTHEW 14:13-21   **MARK 6:30-44**   LUKE 9:10-17   **JOHN 6:1-13**

In this section, *Feeding the Five Thousand*, you should study Mark 6:30-44 and John 6:1-13, and refer to Matthew and Luke only if you have time or want to dig deeper.

Some questions have a number of parts to them, and you should write your answers to these subsections on the line *above* the question or statement. An example is:

16. Contrast the difference between the disciples' response to the crowds and Jesus' response.

They had no concern for the people and wanted Jesus
DISCIPLES' RESPONSE
to send them away to their homes. There they
could buy their own food and the disciples
wouldn't have to bother.

Jesus' response was one of compassion because
JESUS' RESPONSE
of the crowd's tiredness and hunger. So He
organized them and through the miracle gave
them more than enough to eat.

You should write your answers to the *Disciples' Response* part on the first four lines (as shown above) and the answers to *Jesus' Response* part on the bottom four lines, beginning on the line *above* each statement.

Since the charts vary considerably, you should follow the specific instructions given for each. None of the charts have vertical lines, so you should write your answers under each of the divisions shown by the instructions at the top and a small space in the line(s) under them and just before them. An example is:

19. While in the Pharisee's home, Jesus taught three subjects. As you study LUKE 14, fill in the chart on the next page.

REFERENCE/ WHAT STIMULATED JESUS TO SPEAK?	WHAT WAS HIS MAIN POINT?	WHAT RESPONSE DOES HE CALL FOR?
14:7-11 The leaders taking the best places in the house.	Let someone else [God] be the one to advance you.	Humility and serving others in practice in everyday living.
14:12-14 The invitation He had to eat at the Pharisee's house.	Invite those who cannot repay you in like manner.	For us to actually serve those who cannot return the favor to us.
14:15-24 A statement by one of the guests about the Kingdom.	Not everyone who is invited into God's kingdom necessarily accepts the invitation.	For us to be out inviting people into the kingdom.

Applications

This study is aimed toward personal application. It is fruitless to study the Word of God without applying its teachings to one's own life. So specific application questions are included in each chapter, various suggestions are made in the *Personal Notes* columns (see later in these instructions), and each chapter ends with a general summary application exercise.

Writing personal applications enables the student to maintain a balance between factual content and application to life. Applications emerge out of facts: Jesus, for example, prayed constantly and often taught about prayer; this combination affected His disciples, for they in turn wanted to learn how to pray and eventually became men of prayer as well. Christian disciples today should also be men and women of prayer, learning from the example and teachings of Jesus.

You may write two kinds of applications—in relation to God and in relation to man. The application in relation to God is that which, when applied, will result in your personal spiritual enrichment and uplift. It may be a promise, a command, or some great truth which deepens your devotion to the Lord; it may lead to some needed correction in your attitudes or actions; or it may in some way strengthen or improve your fellowship with God. This application pertains mainly to your own spiritual life.

The application in relation to man is that which, when applied, would improve your relationship to fellow Christians or to those outside of Christ. In general, this application pertains to your ministry and service for the Lord.

In writing your applications, jot down in detail the way you might apply to your life a certain truth from the portion of this study—chapter, half a chapter, a few sections—you are studying. You should write your application on a single thought, whether drawn from one verse, several verses, an extended passage, or the whole study. You will benefit more from enlarging on one application than from merely mentioning several challenges.

Use personal, singular pronouns "I," "me," "my," and "mine." Make your application practical by describing how you will put in practice the truth under consideration. Avoid writing in a general way about truths which should be specifically applied. It is profitable to state what action you plan to take when writing your application (see Psalm 119:59).

The following four questions may help you write meaningful applications:

1. What is the truth I want to apply to my life?
2. What is my need?
3. What is my plan of action?
4. How can I check my progress?

A sample application might be written like this: "When Jesus said, 'Love your neighbor as yourself,' He meant for all of us to do so. I will apply this truth to my life by deliberately showing my love to Joe and Sam this week, helping them with their problem of transportation by going to their homes and picking them up. To make sure that I do it, I will call them, make the arrangements, and then mark my calendar with their addresses and times when I will be picking them up."

The habitual practice of writing applications is one of the most healthful exercises for spiritual growth. In a unique way it can clarify areas where we can improve, and provide means from the Word, particularly from the life and ministry of Jesus, for doing so. When followed by definite action, this practice becomes a stepping-stone to a fruitful life that glorifies the Lord. The result should contribute to a "conscience clear before God and man" (Acts 24:16).

Maps

Each chapter in each book of the study has a map of a portion of Palestine at its beginning. On these maps you will locate the places where activities of the chapter occurred during Jesus' ministry in first century Palestine. The maps in Chapter 1 of Book I and Chapter 4 of Book III are general location maps only, to acquaint you with Jesus' world. The other maps ask you to find specific locations discussed in that particular chapter.

To get the feel of what is happening at the location you are studying, fill out these maps at the start of your study. This exercise will also give you an idea of the distances Jesus and His disciples traveled as you actually put yourself "on location."

Use the maps in your Bible or purchase an inexpensive paperback Bible atlas. Two are readily available:
1. *Atlas of the Bible Lands,* C. S. Hammond & Co., Maplewood, New Jersey, 1959.
2. John Stirling, *An Atlas of the Life of Christ,* George Philip & Son Limited, London, 1966. (Distributed by the Fleming H. Revell Company, Old Tappan, New Jersey).

Personal Notes

A special feature of these studies is the *Personal Notes* column in the outside margin of each study page. It is not identified as such, but a 2¼-inch space is provided for these notes. Record in this column any additional thoughts or insights you might have while doing the study or participating in a discussion on it. Following are some specific suggestions, things you may want to watch for as you do the study.
1. *Definition*—define any words or concepts you do not understand.
2. *Application Ideas*—jot down thoughts as you go along, on things you would like to apply to your life.
3. *Cross-references*—write down references of other Scriptures that concern the things you are studying.
4. *Observation (Personal Insight)*—record ideas, insights, or observations that come to you while you are studying a question, chart, or section.
5. *Question*—write out questions, difficulties, or problems you have, things you do not understand. Perhaps you can study them later or bring them up in your discussion for clarification.
6. *Future Study*—note items you may want to study further in the future.

You will find examples of each of the above suggestions throughout the studies, written in longhand in the *Personal Notes* columns. An example of *each* of the six categories appears in Chapter 1.

You may make notes in these columns either as you are answering the questions or filling out the charts, or you may go back through the study after you have finished a whole section or the entire study. Or you may use a combination of both, varying your study as you see fit. Since the charts have to do with a great deal of material, you may want to use the *Personal Notes* columns near them for further notes. The variety of possibilities for these columns is great, so be sure to use them freely.

THIS Bible study is not the product of a single individual who was challenged to create a study on the life and ministry of Jesus Christ, and who then retired to his study to write it. It is, rather, the product of the diligent work of many men and women around the world: a team of Navigator staff who realized the need for this study and began putting it together; many staff and contacts worldwide who field tested the first draft and made many excellent recommendations; the team and an editor who worked hard on a second draft; more field testing on the second draft and more recommendations; the team and another editor who put together the final draft; more people who field tested the charts and diagrams; still others who, because of their interest in the study, read it and offered valuable advice.

To all who have prayed and labored diligently, a hearty word of thanks. It is, in every sense, the result of a team effort, coached and coordinated by the Holy Spirit. As the Author of the Word of God, as Teacher and Interpreter of that Word to believers, and as the divine distributor of His gifts to them, the Holy Spirit has in a unique way directed the production of this study. His desire for its effectiveness must stem from His special ministry of revealing and glorifying Jesus Christ in our lives. To this purpose the study is dedicated.

"I have much more to say to you," Jesus said, *"more than you can now bear. But when He, the Spirit of truth, comes, He will guide you into all truth. He will not speak on His own; He will speak only what He hears, and He will tell you what is yet to come. He will bring glory to Me by taking from what is Mine and making it known to you. All that belongs to the Father is Mine. That is why I said the Spirit will take from what is Mine and make it known to you."*
JOHN 16:12-15

RISING OPPOSITION

Locate and label the sites where the following events took place. Use small arrows to indicate the travels of Jesus:

1. Last location from Book I, Chapter 6 (the Sermon on the Mount)
2. Healing the centurion's servant (Matthew 8:5–13)
3. Raising the widow's son from the dead (Luke 7:11–17)
4. Anointing by a sinful woman (Luke 7:36–50)
5. Opposition from the religious leaders (Matthew 12:22–45)
6. Teaching by parables (Matthew 13:1–53)
7. Stilling the storm (Mark 4:35–41)

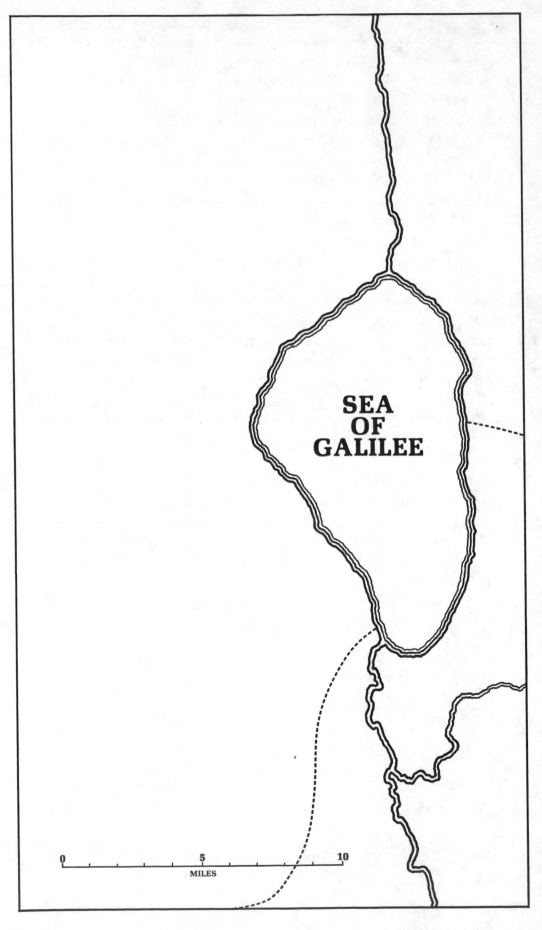

SEA OF GALILEE

0   5   10
MILES

OPPOSITION TO JESUS' MINISTRY

I will open my mouth in a parable; I will utter dark sayings of old, Which we have heard and known, And our fathers have told us.
PSALM 78:2-3

Following the Sermon on the Mount, Jesus returned to the fishing village of Capernaum, which He had made His home. But again privacy and rest eluded Him, since many people came to Him to have their physical and spiritual needs met.

MATTHEW 8:5-13   LUKE 7:1-10

Healing the Centurion's Servant

Jesus astonished His listeners with both the content of His teaching and the authority with which He spoke. As He walked down from the Mount, a great crowd of people followed Him. When He entered Capernaum, the representative of a Roman centurion approached Him. As the commander of 100 soldiers in the Roman army, the centurion was a man of authority. While the Jews hated most Gentiles, the people of Capernaum loved this centurion because of his many good deeds in the community.

QUESTION: Why would a Roman soldier be kind to Jews?

1. What is the relationship between faith and humility as demonstrated by the centurion?

_____

_____

_____

2. How did Jesus use this example of faith to teach the multitudes?

_____

_____

_____

LUKE 7:11-17

Raising a Widow's Son

Soon afterward, Jesus, still followed by the crowds, came to the little town of Nain, a few miles southeast of Nazareth. As He entered the city, a funeral procession of the only son of a widow passed by. The death of that son meant not only the loss of someone to care and provide for the widow, but also the end of the family name.

When Jesus raised the young man from the dead, He risked defilement by touching the bier on which the corpse was carried. In so doing, He broke Jewish law and violated Jewish practice. "Certain procedures were practiced at Jewish funerals that were in marked contrast to the approach of Jesus. Mourners were hired to chant a lament. This was designed not as a comfort to the bereaved, but as a measure of the respect in which the dead person was held. There was little attempt to relieve the sorrow."[1]

3. What insights do you gain about Jesus' nature when you compare and contrast the healing of the centurion's servant and the raising of the widow's son?

_____

_____

_____

_____

Reassuring John the Baptist

FUTURE STUDY: What kind of a person was this Herod?

MATTHEW 11:2–30	LUKE 7:18–35

News of Jesus' activities swept the countryside, reaching even Herod's palace at Machaerus in Perea where John the Baptist was imprisoned. He had been in captivity for nearly a year, and had begun to have doubts about the messiahship of Jesus. So he sent some of his disciples to Jesus to ask if He indeed was the Promised Messiah. (Why John was in prison will be studied in the next chapter.)

4. What do you think could have caused John to question whether Jesus was "the One to come"?

_____

_____

_____

5. How did Jesus answer John's doubts and help restore his faith?

_____

_____

_____

1. From *Jesus the Messiah* by Donald Guthrie, page 98. Copyright © 1972 by The Zondervan Corporation. Used by permission.

6. What did Jesus say about John before the crowds? Why?

_____

_____

_____

7. What does Jesus say about His own relationship to the Father?
(MATTHEW 11:25-27)

_____

_____

_____

8. What do you think is the yoke and burden of Jesus? (11:29-30) How
do you take it?

_____

_____

_____

_____

_____

LUKE 7:36—8:3

Anointing by a Sinful Woman

Jesus, invited to a Pharisee's house to eat, was approached by a sinful woman while He was reclining at the table. "This woman was neither Mary of Bethany (John 12:1-8) nor Mary Magdalene. She was an unchaste woman (verse 37), a prostitute likely converted under John's or Jesus' ministry . . . . The Oriental banquet was in a Pharisee's house. Guests reclined, so it was easy for the woman to wash Jesus' feet with her tears and anoint them."[2]

9. Why did the Pharisee react as he did to the woman's anointing
Jesus?

_____

_____

_____

_____

2 Merrill F. Unger, Unger's Bible Handbook (Chicago: Moody Press, 1966), page 524.

10. What was Jesus' reaction to her anointing Him?

_____

_____

_____

11. What was Jesus teaching Simon in this incident?

APPLICATION:
What is Jesus
teaching me
through this
incident?

_____

_____

_____

Luke states that several women accompanied Jesus and His disciples on a preaching trip through Galilee (8:1–3). Touched by Jesus' ministry, these women now traveled with Him and the crowds, providing money for His needs along the way.

Dealing with False Accusations

MATTHEW 12:22-45   MARK 3:19b-30

As Jesus ministered to the people, a blind and dumb demon-possessed man was brought to Him. Jesus healed the man, sparking a new round of accusations against Him by the Pharisees.

Though the New Testament says very little about the origin, nature, characteristics, or ways of demons, they are a present reality. In Scripture, the demon is an ethically evil being, who belongs to the kingdom of Satan, or Beelzebub, and opposes God and His plans.

12. What must have been in the minds of the Jewish leaders that prompted them to make this blasphemous accusation?

_____

_____

_____

_____

13. What was the meaning of Jesus' reply to their accusation?

_____

_____

_____

This encounter with the Jewish leaders marked a turning point in Jesus' teaching ministry. Because the leaders were now determined to destroy Him, He would shortly begin teaching in parables or coded messages which could be understood only by those who believed in Him and therefore had "ears to hear" (Mark 4:9).

14. What is the significance of Jesus' answer to the scribes and Pharisees after they demanded a sign from Him? (MATTHEW 12:38-45)

_____

_____

_____

_____

15. As a summary to this section on opposition, in what ways is Jesus greater than . . .

THE TEMPLE? (MATTHEW 12:6)

_____

_____

JONAH? (12:41)

_____

_____

SOLOMON? (12:42)

_____

_____

MATTHEW 12:46-50   MARK 3:31-35   LUKE 8:19-21

Jesus' Family Seeks Him

While Jesus was being opposed by the Pharisees and refusing to give them the spectacular sign they demanded, His family arrived and asked to see Him privately. Jesus had four brothers and at least two sisters (Matthew 13:55-56); Joseph was probably dead, and the family was now living in Capernaum where Jesus had moved them.

"These brothers were friendly toward Jesus earlier in His ministry (John 2:12); but after He was rejected in Nazareth (Luke 4:16-31) there seems to have developed in them a disbelief as to His claims; and later on they ridiculed Him, calling Him the 'Secret Messiah'

OBSERVATION: Two of these brothers would later write New Testament books— James and Jude.

(John 7:5). At the present juncture they were unbelieving and indifferent, not to say hostile, or at least ready to interfere with His work in favor of a kind of quiet and respectable life for the family."[3]

16. What did Jesus mean by His response concerning His family?

_____

_____

_____

17. Who is related to Jesus, according to this passage?

_____

_____

_____

Teaching by Parables

DEFINITION:
A parable is a story used to teach some higher spiritual truth.

MATTHEW 13:1-53   MARK 4:1-34   LUKE 8:4-18

Because of the opposition Jesus was now encountering, He began teaching by parables. Enthusiastic crowds still followed Him, so He climbed into a boat, and taught them as they sat on the shore of the Sea of Galilee. What the crowds did not understand, Jesus explained to His disciples.

The parables of the kingdom, though not all spoken at the same time or publicly, form an invaluable series on the kingdom's origin, character, and development in this imperfect earthly situation, climaxing in perfection at the end.

18. Fill in the following chart concerning this group of Jesus' parables. (Not every blank will necessarily be filled.)

REFERENCES/ TITLE OF THE PARABLE	TO WHAT DO THE MAIN FIGURES IN THE PARABLE REFER?	BRIEFLY STATE THE PRINCIPLE ILLUSTRATED BY THE PARABLE
MATTHEW 13:1-23 MARK 4:1-20 LUKE 8:4-15		

3. J. W. Shepard, *The Christ of the Gospels* (Grand Rapids, Michigan: William B. Eerdmans Publishing Company, 1939), page 219.

REFERENCES/ TITLE OF THE PARABLE	TO WHAT DO THE MAIN FIGURES IN THE PARABLE REFER?	BRIEFLY STATE THE PRINCIPLE ILLUSTRATED BY THE PARABLE
MARK 4:21–25 LUKE 8:16–18		
MARK 4:26–29		
MATTHEW 13:24–30 **MATTHEW 13:36–43**		
MATTHEW 13:31–32 MARK 4:30–32		
MATTHEW 13:33		

REFERENCES/ TITLE OF THE PARABLE	TO WHAT DO THE MAIN FIGURES IN THE PARABLE REFER?	BRIEFLY STATE THE PRINCIPLE ILLUSTRATED BY THE PARABLE
MATTHEW 13:44		
MATTHEW 13:45–46		
MATTHEW 13:47–50		
MATTHEW 13:51–53		

19. Using the principles you have discovered in this chart, record what you have learned about the origin, character, and development of God's kingdom.

_____

_____

_____

_____

_____

CROSS REFERENCES:
1 Chronicles 29:11
1 Corinthians 15:24

MATTHEW 8:23-27   MARK 4:35-41   LUKE 8:22-25

Stilling a Tempest

When He finished teaching the multitudes, Jesus told His disciples to sail across the Sea of Galilee to the eastern shore. (This "sea" is actually a fresh-water lake situated 700 feet below sea level in a valley surrounded by mountains. As cool air dropped down from these mountains, it often caused strong winds, high waves, and sudden storms.)

20. Visualize yourself as one of the disciples. Describe your feelings and reactions as you live through this experience.

_____

_____

_____

_____

_____

21. Review the chapter and your *Personal Notes* column, looking for a principle or truth you feel God wants you to apply in your life. Write out the application and any specific steps you intend to take:

_____

_____

_____

_____

_____

_____

_____

_____

GROWTH OF THE MINISTRY

Locate and label the sites where the following events took place. Use small arrows to indicate the travels of Jesus:

1. Last location from previous chapter
2. Curing the demoniac (Mark 5:1–20)
3. Healing Jairus' daughter (Matthew 9:18–26)
4. Rejection of Jesus (Mark 6:1–6)
5. Sending out the Twelve (Mark 6:7–13)
6. Return of the Twelve (Mark 6:30)
7. Feeding the 5,000 (Mark 6:34–44)
8. Walking on the water (Mark 6:45–52)
9. Discourse on the Bread of Life (John 6:22–71)

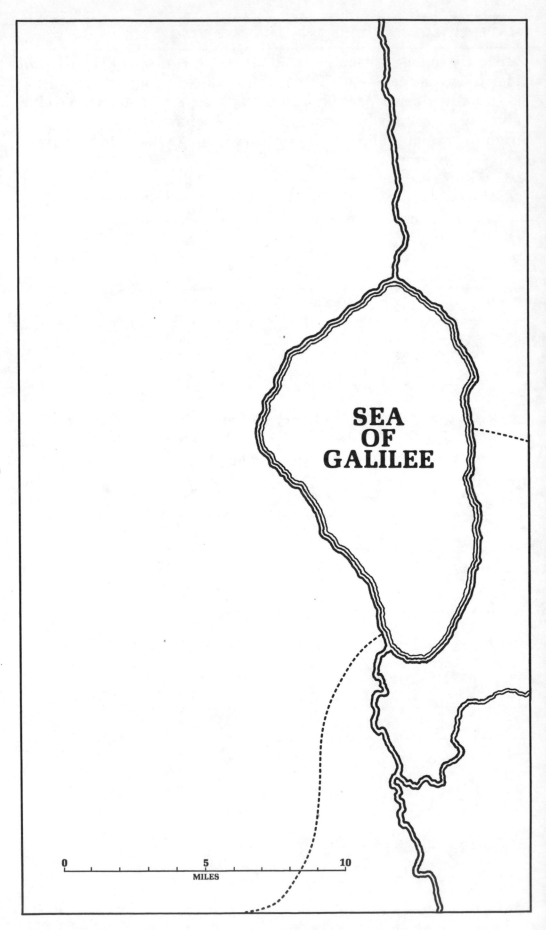

SEA OF GALILEE

0   5   10
MILES

EXPANSION OF JESUS' MINISTRY

And all your sons will be taught of the Lord; And the well-being of your sons will be great.
ISAIAH 54:13

After the events of the preceding day, the disciples of Jesus were profoundly impressed. "They feared exceedingly and no wonder. Here was one who in the same day had cured a blind-dumb lunatic, met the learned Scribes and Pharisees in debate and defeated them, taught many wonderful things in beautiful but half-enigmatic parables, and [then] with a word [made] the cyclonic winds cease and [calmed] the raging sea. They were filled with amazement. . . .

"They were growing in their apprehension and comprehension of Jesus, but they had much to learn yet and needed to grow in the knowledge of the *Lord* Jesus Christ. At least they had caught one more glimpse of His majesty and were filled with dread and wonder. He was not just the human Jesus then; He was also the divine Christ."[1]

Jesus now led His band of disciples into the non-Jewish territory of the Decapolis.

MATTHEW 8:28-34   MARK 5:1-20   **LUKE 8:26-39**

Curing a Demoniac

Jesus and His disciples reached the eastern side of the Sea of Galilee near Gergasa (see the map in this chapter). "Suddenly, weird terrifying shrieks rent the night air. Darting from behind the tombs, two demoniacs swiftly bore down on the little group. One of them was notorious and utterly uncontrollable. Men had tried using chains to tame him, but he shattered the links to pieces. His frenzied strength was phenomenal, and no one dared to pass where he lived. The disciples must have been terrified . . . . Or had their faith grown stronger since the stilling of the storm? . . . Surely the disciples were also overawed by the dignity and authority of Jesus as He stood facing the advancing demoniacs.

"Mark and Luke concentrate on the more notorious demoniac, but Matthew includes them both. There are other stories where Matthew included two and the other writers mentioned only one (e.g., two blind men at Jericho; two asses at the entry into Jerusalem)."[2]

1. J. W. Shepard, *The Christ of the Gospels* (Grand Rapids, Michigan: William B. Eerdmans Publishing Company, 1939), page 234.
2. From *Jesus the Messiah* by Donald Guthrie, pages 110-11. Copyright © 1972 by The Zondervan Corporation. Used by permission.

1. Describe the demon-possessed man before and after Jesus dealt with him.

BEFORE
_____

_____

_____

_____

AFTER
_____

_____

_____

2. Describe your life before and after you met Jesus Christ.

BEFORE
_____

_____

_____

_____

AFTER
_____

_____

_____

3. What was the reaction of the herdsmen to the situation? Why?

_____

_____

_____

4. Why do you think Jesus did not take the former demoniac with Him?

_____

_____

_____

MATTHEW 9:18-35   **MARK 5:21-43**   LUKE 8:40-56

Raising Jairus' Daughter

After healing the Gadarene demoniac, Jesus and His disciples returned to Capernaum by boat (Mark 5:21). As usual, the crowds were waiting for Him and welcomed His return (Luke 8:40).

Although most Jewish leaders were hostile to Jesus, Jairus, a ruler of the synagogue in Capernaum, asked Jesus to heal his dying daughter. (The supervisors who controlled services in the synagogues were known as rulers. Their duties included the selection of who was to read from the Law and the Prophets and who was to preach. They also led discussions and generally kept order.)

As He was following Jairus to his house, Jesus stopped to heal a woman. During this delay, the ruler's daughter died.

5. How do you think Jairus felt as each of the following occurrences took place?

MARK 5:22-24

_____

_____

_____

MARK 5:25-34

_____

_____

_____

MARK 5:35-37

_____

_____

_____

MARK 5:38-43

_____

_____

_____

6. What characteristics of Jesus are demonstrated by these two incidents?

_____

_____

_____

_____

**Nazareth's
Second
Rejection
of Jesus**

MATTHEW 13:54-58   **MARK 6:1-6**

After Jesus raised Jairus' daughter from the dead, He healed two blind men and cured a demoniac (Matthew 9:27-35). Then He paid His last recorded visit to Nazareth.

7. Why did the Nazarenes reject Jesus?

_____

_____

_____

8. What were the results of this rejection?

_____

_____

**Sending out
the Twelve**

MATTHEW 9:36—11:1 MARK 6:7-13   LUKE 9:1-6

Jesus left Nazareth and went again among the cities of Galilee "teaching in their synagogues, preaching the good news of the Kingdom and healing every kind of disease and sickness" (Matthew 9:35). At this point, He sent the twelve apostles out on a special assignment.

9. How did Jesus respond to the multitudes He encountered? (MATTHEW 9:36—10:1)

_____

_____

_____

10. List the instructions given to the Twelve (MATTHEW 10:5-23).

WHAT TO SAY
_____

WHAT TO EXPECT
_____

WHERE TO GO
_____

WHAT TO TAKE
_____

_____

WHAT TO DO
_____

11. What are some characteristic actions and attitudes of a disciple?
    (MATTHEW 10:24-42)

_____

_____

_____

_____

_____

_____

_____

   After receiving their instructions, the disciples went out
as Jesus had commanded them (Mark 6:12; Luke 9:6). Jesus Himself
continued teaching and preaching in the villages of Galilee
(Matthew 11:1).

MATTHEW 14:1-12   **MARK 6:14-29**   LUKE 9:7-9

About this time, Herod Antipas had John the Baptist beheaded. John
had been imprisoned nearly a year in the dungeon of a fortification
called Machaerus, east of the Dead Sea.

Death of John the Baptist

12. Why was John in prison?

_____

_____

13. Why was he killed?

_____

_____

14. Match Herod's actions (MARK 6:17-29) with each of the three areas of sin in 1 JOHN 2:15-16.

_____

_____

_____

_____

_____

_____

_____

15. What did Herod think when he heard what Jesus was doing and saying?

_____

_____

_____

Feeding the Five Thousand

MATTHEW 14:13-21   **MARK 6:30-44**   LUKE 9:10-17   **JOHN 6:1-13**

The twelve apostles returned and reported their experiences while ministering in the cities of Galilee (Mark 6:30; Luke 9:10). Jesus then went with them across the Sea of Galilee to a quiet place for rest. Perhaps, as part of the training of His men, Jesus wanted to evaluate the results of the mission on which He had just sent them.

Instead of finding a place to rest, however, Jesus and His disciples were once again surrounded by the crowds.

16. Contrast the difference between the disciples' response to the crowds and Jesus' response.

_____

DISCIPLES' RESPONSE

_____

_____

_____

JESUS' RESPONSE

_____

_____

_____

APPLICATION: How do I respond when I'm tired?

17. Write a brief newspaper article about this incident as if you had actually been a reporter witnessing the event. Include a headline.

_____

_____

_____

_____

_____

_____

_____

_____

MATTHEW 14:22-36   MARK 6:45-56   **JOHN 6:14-21**

Jesus Walks on Water

The feeding of the 5,000 brought such a response from the crowds that they were ready to take Jesus and force Him to be king. Later that evening, Jesus went into the hills alone to pray and ordered His disciples to return to Bethsaida, on the other side of the sea. But due to a strong wind which had come up against them, the disciples had, by three o'clock in the morning, sailed no more than three or four miles.

18. What do Matthew and John add to the account given in Mark's Gospel?

MATTHEW 14:22-36
_____

_____

JOHN 6:14-21
_____

_____

19. What lessons do you think Jesus was trying to teach His disciples?

_____

_____

_____

Discourse on the Bread of Life

After calming the storm and the disciples' hearts, Jesus and His men reached the northwestern shore at Gennesaret, where He was again confronted by large crowds. Here He healed many people. Because of His concern that these crowds were following Him from the wrong motive—that they were more interested in physical bread than the life of godliness He presented—He challenged their devotion in His discourse on the bread of life.

20. At five points during this discourse there were reactions from the crowd. Indicate these on the chart below, and describe the situation from the references given.

WHAT JESUS SAID THAT CAUSED THE REACTION	WHO REACTED	DESCRIBE THE REACTION
JOHN 6:22-40	JOHN 6:41-42	
JOHN 6:41-51	JOHN 6:52	
JOHN 6:52-59	JOHN 6:60-61	

WHAT JESUS SAID THAT CAUSED THE REACTION	WHO REACTED	DESCRIBE THE REACTION
JOHN 6:60-65	JOHN 6:66	
JOHN 6:67	JOHN 6:68-69	

21. Summarize Jesus' teaching about Himself in this discourse, and tell how it can be applied to your everyday life.

_____

_____

_____

_____

_____

22. Review the chapter and your *Personal Notes* column, looking for a principle or truth you feel God wants you to apply to your life. Write out the application and any specific steps you intend to take:

_____

_____

_____

_____

_____

_____

CONTINUED OPPOSITION

Locate and label the sites where the following events took place. Use small arrows to indicate the travels of Jesus:

1. Last location from previous chapter
2. Controversy with the Pharisees (Mark 7:1–23)
3. Healing the Canaanite woman's daughter (Mark 7:24–30)
4. Feeding the 4,000 (Mark 8:1–10)
5. The Pharisees demand a sign (Mark 8:11–12)
6. Healing a blind man (Mark 8:22–26)

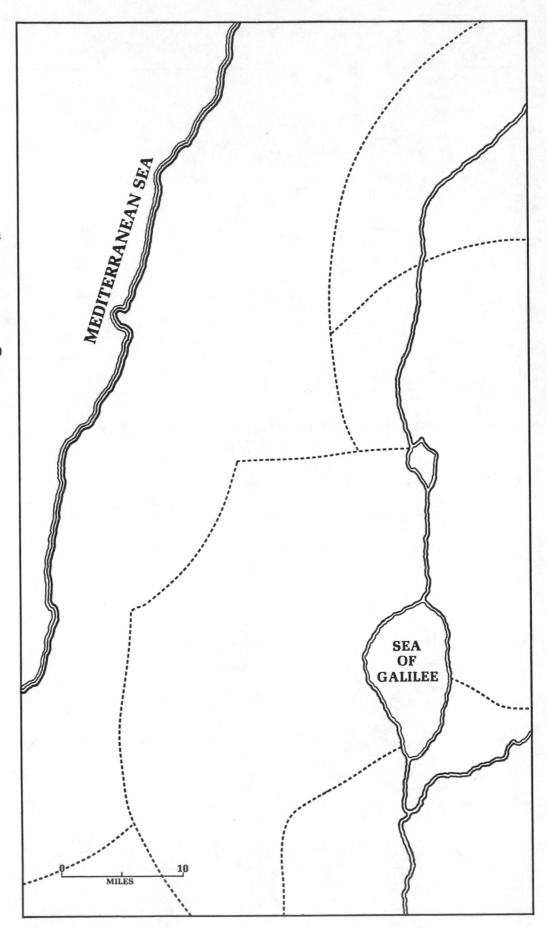

MEDITERRANEAN SEA

SEA OF GALILEE

0   10
MILES

FURTHER CLASHES WITH THE PHARISEES

A bruised reed He will not break, And a dimly burning wick He will not extinguish; He will faithfully bring forth justice.
ISAIAH 42:3

By this time Jesus had become well-known throughout Palestine and the surrounding areas. Although He was popular with the crowds, the religious leaders hated Him and created controversy whenever they could. As you study this chapter, look for reasons why Jesus was popular and for causes of the rising tensions between Him and the Pharisees.

MATTHEW 15:1-20   MARK 7:1-23   JOHN 7:1

Exposing Hypocrisy

Evidently Jesus' ministry had caused a stir as far away as Jerusalem, for some Jewish leaders made the trip from the capital to Galilee to ask Him some questions.

1. Why wasn't Jesus concerned that His disciples observe the tradition of washing their hands?

_____

_____

_____

2. What is the difference between a commandment of God and tradition?

_____

_____

_____

_____

"Whatever was most spiritual, living, human and grand in the Scriptures they (the Pharisees) passed by. Generation after generation the commentaries of their famous men multiplied, and the pupils studied the commentaries instead of the text. Moreover, it was a rule with them that the correct interpretation of a passage was as authoritative as the text itself; and, the interpretations of the famous masters being as a matter of course believed to be correct, the mass of opinions which were held to be as precious as the Bible itself grew to enormous proportions. These were 'the traditions of the elders.' "[1]

"It [Corban] is the most general term for a sacrifice of any kind. In the course of time it became associated with an objectionable practice. Anything dedicated to the temple by pronouncing the votive word Corban forthwith belonged to the temple, but only ideally; actually it might remain in the possession of him who made the vow. So a son might be justified in not supporting his old parents simply because he designated his property or a part of it as a gift to the temple, that is, as [Corban]. There was no necessity for fulfilling his vow, yet he was actually prohibited from ever using his property for the support of his parents."[2]

3. Why did Jesus rebuke the Jews for their use of the Corban tradition? (MARK 7:9-14)

_____

_____

_____

_____

4. What was wrong with the Pharisees' attitude?

_____

_____

_____

_____

5. How did Jesus respond to the statement that He offended the Pharisees?

_____

_____

_____

_____

1. James Stalker, *Life of Christ* (Old Tappan, New Jersey: Fleming H. Revell Company, 1909), page 29.
2. William Baur, "Corban," *The International Standard Bible Encyclopedia* (Grand Rapids, Michigan: William B. Eerdmans Publishing Company, 1956), page 709.

6. Why didn't the disciples understand the parable?

_____

_____

_____

7. What commands of God might *we* tend to set aside by a current "Christian tradition"? How?

_____

_____

_____

_____

_____

MATTHEW 15:21-28 MARK 7:24-30

Jesus at this time withdrew to Tyre and Sidon. This territory and its major centers, immediately north of Galilee, were coastal cities of Phoenicia and a part of the Roman province of Syria. In this Gentile territory a pagan woman came to Jesus, seeking healing for her daughter.

"She was a Grecian from the district of Syro-Phoenicia. She had a young daughter possessed by demons. Reports of Jesus had spread as far as Tyre and Sidon (cf. Mark 3:8). The woman had probably decided what she would do if Jesus ever came into her vicinity. The main feature of the narrative concerns her meeting with Jesus and begging Him to do something. Matthew gives her urgent plea, 'Have mercy on me, O Lord, Son of David; my daughter is severely possessed by a demon.' It is strange that a Gentile should use the title 'Son of David,' but she obviously knew something about Jewish affairs."[3]

Healing the Canaanite Woman's Daughter

FUTURE STUDY: Do a research study on demons and demon-possession.

8. Why do you think Jesus went to Tyre?

_____

_____

_____

_____

3. From *Jesus the Messiah* by Donald Guthrie, pages 158-59. Copyright © 1972 by The Zondervan Corporation. Used by permission.

9. What is revealed about the following people's attitudes?

WOMAN

_____

_____

DISCIPLES

_____

_____

JESUS

_____

_____

10. What was significant about this event?

_____

_____

_____

_____

_____

_____

**Feeding
the Four
Thousand**

MATTHEW 15:29-39   MARK 7:31—8:10

"How long Jesus and His apostles remained in the borders of Tyre is unknown. Possibly the fame of the miracle forced Him to leave sooner than He had proposed. He did not return south to Capernaum, but took His way in a north-easterly direction, up through the region of Sidon. He likely followed the caravan road from the region of Sidon on the south side of the river Bostrenus, crossing a lofty spur of the Lebanon range amidst peaks six thousand feet high, and passed over the natural rock-bridge spanning the Leontes [River] . . . .

"His destination was further to the south, in the borders of Decapolis, the territory of the ten allied Greek free cities."[4]

Here the people brought to Jesus a deaf man who was also a stammerer. Taking him aside from the multitude, Jesus gradually healed him. First He put His fingers into the man's ears and touched his tongue with a finger moistened with saliva. Then He said, "Ephatha" (Aramaic for "Be thou unbarred"). The Gentile crowds were astonished at this miracle, and as the news spread the multitudes of these "other sheep" not of the Jewish fold increased. They remained without food for three days, sleeping on the ground at night and pressing to see and hear Jesus during the day. Because

4. J. W. Shepard, *The Christ of the Gospels* (Grand Rapids, Michigan: William B. Eerdmans Publishing Company, 1939), page 289.

Jesus felt sorry for the people's hungry condition, He worked another spectacular miracle.

11. Compare the feeding of the 4,000 with the feeding of the 5,000 (see JOHN 6:3-14).

THE 4,000	THE 5,000
D I F F E R E N C E S	
S I M I L A R I T I E S	

12. What are two or three principles concerning your life and ministry you can draw from both these incidents?

_____

_____

_____

_____

MATTHEW 16:1-12   MARK 8:11-21

The Leaven of the Pharisees

From the Decapolis Jesus headed toward Caesarea of Philippi stopping along the way at Magdala (also called Magadon and Dalmanutha). There He used a discussion with the religious leaders as an opportunity to teach His disciples.

13. Why did the Pharisees and Sadducees ask for a sign?

_____

_____

14. What was Jesus' response?

_____

_____

15. What is the meaning of this parable?

_____

_____

_____

16. Explain the "sign of Jonah."

_____

_____

_____

The leaven used in biblical times served the same function as yeast does today. A small lump of dough called leaven was saved from every batch. The next time dough was made this small lump was used to make it rise; then a new lump was saved for the next baking.

17. Why did Jesus compare the teaching of the Pharisees and Sadducees to leaven?

_____

_____

_____

18. Why did Jesus reprove the disciples for lack of faith?

_____

_____

Healing a Blind Man

MARK 8:22-26

Mark records an additional stop in Bethsaida, en route to Caesarea Philippi, where Jesus healed a blind man in an unusual way. In some ways this healing resembled that of the deaf man at the Decapolis. In both cases Jesus took the men aside, used spittle, healed gradually, and told them not to tell others.

19. What was unique about this healing?

_____

_____

_____

20. What significance can be attached to this uniqueness?

_____

_____

_____

21. Why, in your opinion, was the man told not to tell others?

_____

_____

_____

22. Review the chapter and your *Personal Notes* column, looking
    for a principle or truth you feel God wants you to apply in your
    life. Write out the application and any specific steps you intend
    to take:

_____

_____

_____

_____

_____

_____

_____

TRAINING DISCIPLES

Locate and label the sites where the following events took place. Use small arrows to indicate the travels of Jesus:

1. Last location from previous chapter
2. Peter's Great Confession (Mark 8:27-30)
3. The Transfiguration (Mark 9:2-13)
4. Healing a demon possessed boy (Mark 9:14-20)
5. Peter and the temple tax (Matthew 17:24-27)
6. Rejection in a village (Luke 9:51-62)

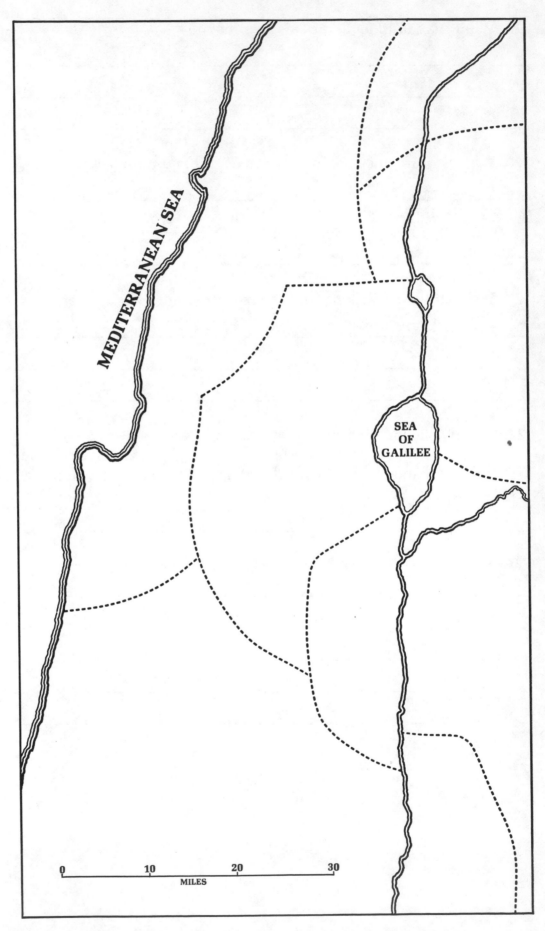

A NEW DIRECTION

And to Him was given dominion, glory and a kingdom, that all the peoples, nations, and men of every language might serve Him. His dominion is an everlasting dominion which will not pass away; and His kingdom is one which will not be destroyed.
DANIEL 7:14

From this point on, the emphasis of Jesus' ministry changes distinctly. "The day at Caesarea Philippi marks the watershed of the Gospels. From this point onwards, the streams begin to flow in another direction. The current of popularity which seemed likely in the earlier days of Jesus' ministry to carry Him to the throne has now been left behind. The tide sets toward the cross. The Galilean sunshine is suddenly clouded over, and the air grows sultry and heavy with the gathering storm. The voices shouting applause die away, and another more ominous note is heard. At Caesarea Jesus stood, as it were, on a dividing-line. It was like a hilltop from which He could see behind Him all the road He had travelled, and in front of Him the dark, forbidding way awaiting Him. One look He cast back to where the afterglow of happy days still lingered, and then faced around and marched forward towards the shadows. His course was now set to Calvary."[1]

MATTHEW 16:13-20   MARK 8:27-30   LUKE 9:18-21

Peter's Great Confession

As the opposition to His ministry grew, Jesus turned His attention to a more intensive training of the Twelve. He asked His disciples a question which is relevant to all ages: "Who do people say that the Son of man is?"

1. Study the replies to Jesus' questions and suggest possible reasons for these answers in the chart below.

THE ANSWERS GIVEN	POSSIBLE REASONS FOR THESE ANSWERS
THEN	

---

1. James S. Stewart, *The Life and Teaching of Jesus Christ* (Edinburgh: The Committee on Publications, the Church of Scotland, 1933), page 116.

THE ANSWERS GIVEN TODAY	POSSIBLE REASONS FOR THESE ANSWERS
PETER	

2. What do you think Jesus meant by His responses to Peter's answer?

"This was not revealed to you by man, but by My Father in heaven"

_____

_____

_____

"You are Peter, and on this rock I will build My church"

DEFINITION: What is the church?

_____

_____

_____

_____

"The gates of Hades will not overcome it"

_____

_____

_____

"I will give you the keys of the kingdom of heaven"

_____

_____

_____

"Whatever you bind on earth will be bound in heaven; and whatever you loose on earth will be loosed in heaven"

_____

_____

_____

3. What is the significance of this passage for today?

_____

_____

_____

_____

MATTHEW 16:21-28   MARK 8:31—9:1   LUKE 9:22-27

Jesus Foretells His Death and Resurrection

When Peter confessed Jesus as the Christ, he represented the conviction of the other disciples. This confession, in turn, opened the way for a new depth to Jesus' teaching. He began to tell the disciples what being the Messiah really meant and what was going to happen to Him.

4. What did Jesus say was going to happen to Him?

_____

_____

_____

5. Why did Jesus reject Peter's rebuke?

_____

_____

_____

6. Fill in the chart below from MATTHEW 16:24-28.

REQUIREMENTS	APPLICATION TO TODAY

The Transfiguration

MATTHEW 17:1-13   MARK 9:2-13   LUKE 9:28-36

Jesus continued to reveal more about Himself to the disciples, singling out three of them to observe His transfiguration.

7. Define the term *transfiguration* (use a Bible dictionary or encyclopedia).

8. While it is impossible to locate the exact place of the transfiguration, it is known to have taken place in the mountains. Why had Jesus gone up into the mountains with Peter, James, and John?

Most commentators believe that Moses represented the Jewish Law and that Elijah represented the Prophets. Their appearance on the mount of transfiguration emphasized that the unity of their messages was found in Jesus as the crucified and resurrected Christ.

9. What significance did Peter attach to this event in later life? (2 PETER 1:16-21)

10. At what other time did God audibly speak about His Son?

_____

_____

11. Compare the two events.

_____

_____

MATTHEW 17:14-21 **MARK 9:14-29** LUKE 9:37-43a

Healing the Demon-possessed Boy

The day after the transfiguration Jesus and the three disciples rejoined the others who were faced with a problem they couldn't handle.

12. Why couldn't the disciples cast out the demon?

_____

_____

_____

13. What can you learn about faith from this episode?

_____

_____

_____

MATTHEW 17:22-23 **MARK 9:30-32** LUKE 9:43b-45

Return to Capernaum

Jesus tried to keep His return journey through Galilee private in order to have more time to teach the disciples. Again He emphasized what the future held for Him.

14. What, in your opinion, is the reason why the disciples were afraid to ask Him questions?

_____

_____

_____

_____

Paying the Temple Tax

MATTHEW 17:24-27

As they returned to Capernaum, Peter was confronted by the tax collector who wanted Jesus' temple tax. Jesus used the situation to teach about Himself.

15. What was the temple tax? (EXODUS 30:11-16)

_____

_____

_____

16. Put yourself in Peter's position. What would you have learned from this experience?

_____

_____

_____

"Jesus, as a Jew, was just as much under obligation to comply with this particular law as with any other. Nor was there any peculiar indignity, either in kind or degree, involved in obeying that law. Doubtless it was a great indignity and humiliation to the Son of God to be paying taxes for the maintenance of His own Father's house!"[2] The important point was that the paying of the tax would serve as a lesson on meekness to the disciples, as well as showing the need of obedience to civil law.

A Discourse by Jesus

MATTHEW 18:1-35   MARK 9:33-50   LUKE 9:46-50

The episode with the temple tax also served as an illustration of humility—the first point of Jesus' discourse.

17. What need in the disciples' lives caused Jesus to present this discourse at this time? (MARK 9:33-37)

_____

_____

_____

---

2. From *The Training of the Twelve* by Alexander Balmain Bruce, pages 224-25. Copyright 1928 by Doubleday, Doran & Company, Inc. Reprinted by permission of the Publisher.

18. Jesus discussed five major topics in this discourse. Study the
passages and complete the chart below.

TOPIC/ REFERENCE	MAJOR TEACHING	ILLUSTRATION USED	YOUR CONCLUSION ABOUT THE TEACHING
HUMILITY MATTHEW 18:1-5			
SIN MATTHEW 18:6-10			
GOD'S CONCERN FOR PEOPLE MATTHEW 18:11-14			
RECONCILIATION MATTHEW 18:15-20			
FORGIVENESS MATTHEW 18:21-35			

Traveling to Jerusalem

MATTHEW 8:18-22 19:1-2	MARK 10:1	LUKE 9:51-62	JOHN 7:2-10

"The visit of Jesus in Galilee after His return from Caesarea Philippi had been brief and of a very private character. All Galilee was now astir in preparation for the annual caravan which would start in a few days to the feast. Jesus had not been in Judea for [some] months. His work of itinerant evangelist in Judea had been cut short at that time because the Jews were seeking to kill Him. . . . He was fully conscious of the near approach of His death, resurrection and ascension on high. He Himself 'set His face with fixedness of purpose' in spite of all difficulty and danger, 'to go to Jerusalem.' "[3]

19. Why did Jesus leave His ministry in Galilee at this time? (LUKE 9:51; see JOHN 7:1-10)

_____

_____

_____

20. Why didn't Jesus make an issue of the Samaritans' failure to receive Him? (LUKE 9:51-56)

_____

_____

_____

21. Along the way, Jesus laid the claims of discipleship on certain men, all of whom had excuses (LUKE 9:57-62). What are some examples today of the three excuses recorded here?

_____

_____

_____

_____

_____

_____

_____

3. J. W. Shepard, *The Christ of the Gospels* (Grand Rapids, Michigan: William B. Eerdmans Publishing Company, 1939), pages 339-41.

22. Review the chapter and your *Personal Notes* column, looking for a principle or truth you feel God wants you to apply in your life. Write out the application and any specific steps you intend to take:

_____

_____

_____

_____

_____

_____

_____

_____

A TIME OF DISCOURSES

Locate and label the sites where the following events took place. Use small arrows to indicate the travels of Jesus:

1. Last location from previous chapter
2. Events during the Feast of Tabernacles (John 7:11—10:21)
3. The seventy sent out (Luke 10:1-24)
4. The story of the good neighbor (Luke 10:25-37)
5. Visiting Mary and Martha (Luke 10:38-42)

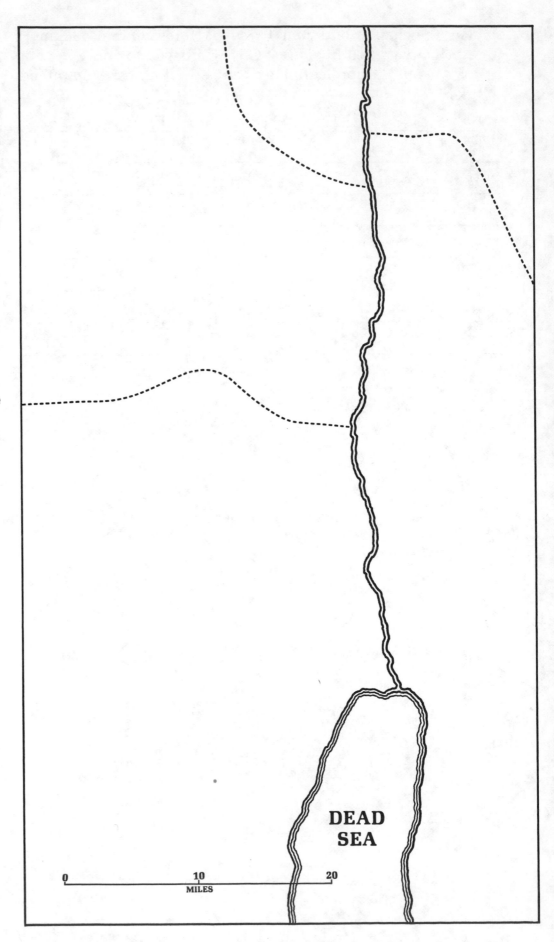

DEAD SEA

0   10   20
MILES

ENCOUNTERS IN JERUSALEM

For He will deliver the needy when he cries for help, The afflicted also, and him who has no helper.
PSALM 72:12

Jesus arrived in Jerusalem and began what has been called the Later Judean Ministry. He taught in the capital city and in the surrounding province of Judea for a period of about three months, from the Feast of Tabernacles to the Feast of Dedication.

Jesus kept His presence in Jerusalem quiet at first, coming out publicly by teaching in the temple area during the middle of the Feast of Tabernacles. This feast came in the Jewish month of Tisri, present-day September/October, and lasted eight days.

"That was the holiest and greatest of the feasts of the Jews, intended to commemorate the wanderings of the Israelites through the desert. . . .

"The feast followed on the heels of the great day of Atonement, when sacrifices were made for all the sins of the people. It was celebrated with great joy, the Law being read daily, and seventy bullocks being sacrificed for the seventy nations of the world, in token of Messianic ingathering of the nations."[1]

JOHN 7:11-53

Discourse on Living Water

During the first seven days of the Feast of Tabernacles, the priests would pour water, from the Pool of Siloam, into the silver basin on the west side of the altar of burnt offering.

"A multitude of pilgrims also marched around the city with music and shouts in commemoration of the taking of Jericho. Others passed the Brook of Siloam to drink, while chanting the words of Isaiah: 'Ho everyone that thirsteth, . . . With joy shall ye draw water from the wells of salvation' (Isaiah 12:3).

"It was near this procession doubtless that Jesus was standing, moved by the enthusiasm of the people, but saddened by the delusion which mistook mere ceremony for religion—the symbol for the reality. Water was a magic word in that sultry dry climate. Raising His voice suddenly until it sounded out in soft clearness over the throng He cried: 'If anyone thirst let him come to Me and let him drink!' He had the water of life for everyone who would come. The water from Siloam was only a type; He offered them the reality."[2]

---

1. J. W. Shepard, *The Christ of the Gospels* (Grand Rapids, Michigan: William B. Eerdmans Publishing Company, 1939), page 339.
2. J. W. Shepard, page 348.

1. List some of the wrong opinions about Jesus revealed in this incident.

_____

_____

_____

_____

_____

2. During the week-long feast Jesus taught a number of times in and around the temple. His discussions with the people and their leaders covered many topics. The chart below will help summarize the subjects Jesus discussed, their main points, and the reactions they provoked.

REFERENCE/ SUBJECT	MAIN POINT	REACTIONS
JOHN 7:14-24		
JOHN 7:25-31		
JOHN 7:32-36		
JOHN 7:37-44		

3. Choose one opinion about Jesus revealed in this passage and give possible reasons for holding it. How did Jesus respond to the people who held this opinion of Him?

_____

_____

_____

_____

_____

_____

4. In light of what they wanted to know and what Jesus said and did, what conclusions about Jesus would those at the Feast of Tabernacles have reached?

_____

_____

_____

_____

_____

JOHN 8:1-11

Mercy for an Adulteress

Motivated by their unsuccessful encounters with Jesus and His stinging remarks, such as His statement that tax collectors and harlots would enter the kingdom of God before them, the Pharisees devised a plan to trap Jesus. They brought before Him a woman caught in the act of adultery, knowing full well, the Old Testament law said that any person caught in that sin should be stoned to death (Leviticus 20:10; Deuteronomy 22:22).

5. How was the scribes' and Pharisees' question about the adulteress an attempt to trap Jesus?

_____

_____

_____

_____

6. How did Jesus' answer to the question affect those involved in the incident?

_____

_____

7. What did Jesus teach through His response to this question?

_____

_____

_____

_____

Jesus' Teaching about Himself

JOHN 8:12–59

Using the preceding incident as a starting point, Jesus began to explain to the crowd who He was and on whose authority He acted.

8. List all statements in this passage where Jesus used the phrase "I am" about Himself, and fill in the chart below.

REFERENCE/ STATEMENT	CONTEXT OF STATEMENT	MEANING OF STATEMENT

_____

REFERENCE/ STATEMENT	CONTEXT OF STATEMENT	MEANING OF STATEMENT

9. What conclusions did the Jews draw from these statements?

_____

_____

_____

_____

_____

10. What conclusions do you draw?

_____

_____

_____

_____

_____

**Healing a
Blind Man**

JOHN 9:1-41

After pointing out the spiritual blindness of the Jews when they did not recognize Him as the Light of the World, Jesus demonstrated His power by bringing light to a man blind since birth.

11. What problem was posed by the disciples' question? (JOHN 9:2)

_____

_____

12. How did Jesus resolve this problem?

_____

_____

13. Several times after he had been healed, the man told others what had happened to him. Describe the situations in which he gave his testimony and the reactions of those who heard him.

REFERENCE	DESCRIPTION
_____	_____
_____	_____
_____	_____
_____	_____
	_____

JOHN 10:1-21

Discourse on the Good Shepherd

Jesus continued to reveal Himself and His work through figures of speech. The Good Shepherd and the Door figures represent Jesus; the sheep figure represents believers.

14. Contrast the characteristics of the Good Shepherd and the bad shepherds.

_____

_____

_____

_____

15. What does this passage teach about Jesus' provision for the believer?

_____

_____

_____

LUKE 10:1-24

Seventy New Laborers

The mission on which Jesus sent the 70 new laborers was probably training for future ministry. (Some manuscripts and versions have 72 workers.)

16. What was their mission, and how did Jesus equip them for their task?

_____

_____

_____

_____

17. What lessons did Jesus teach the 70 through this experience?

_____

_____

_____

**The Good
Neighbor**

LUKE 10:25–37

When asked how a man could qualify for eternal life, Jesus responded by referring to the Law in terms of *doing* it. He then illustrated His point by telling one of His best known stories.

18. What do the lawyer's questions reveal about him?

_____

_____

_____

"The road from Jerusalem to Jericho descended more than three thousand feet in less than fifteen miles through gorges that were infested with robbers."[3] "The priest and the Levite feared ceremonial defilement from what might have been a corpse for all they knew. This would have cost them the purchase of ashes of a red heifer for purification, the loss of Temple privileges such as eating from the Temple sacrifices during a week of defilement, the arrangement of burial for the corpse, and the rending of a perfectly good garment as a sign of grief. The priest and the Levite quite clearly saw in the victim a threat of personal loss and inconvenience."[4]

*OBSERVATION:
What a
statement on
non-involvement!*

19. How does the response of the Good Samaritan illustrate loving your neighbor as yourself? How can you apply this lesson to your life today?

_____

_____

_____

_____

_____

_____

_____

_____

3. J. McNicol, "The Gospel According to Luke," *The New Bible Commentary* (Grand Rapids, Michigan: William B. Eerdmans Publishing Company 1965), page 851.
4. From *A Survey of the New Testament* by Robert H. Gundry, page 164. Copyright © 1970 by Zondervan Publishing House. Used by permission.

LUKE 10:38-42

Visiting Mary and Martha

While the story of the Good Samaritan emphasizes the importance of good deeds, Jesus' visit to the home of Mary and Martha emphasizes the importance of meditation and time with Him.

20. What were some of the differences between Mary and Martha?

_____

_____

_____

_____

QUESTION: What conflicts have I experienced between service and devotion? How do I solve them?

21. How did Jesus evaluate the responses of the two women?

_____

_____

_____

22. Review the chapter and your *Personal Notes* column looking for a principle or truth you feel God wants you to apply in your life. Write out the application and any specific steps you intend to take:

_____

_____

_____

_____

_____

_____

_____

_____

TEACHING DESPITE OPPOSITION

Locate and label the sites where the following events took place. Use small arrows to indicate the travels of Jesus:

1. Last location from previous chapter
2. Discourse on prayer (Luke 11:1-13)
3. Opposition by the leaders (Luke 11:14-36)
4. Denunciation of the leaders (Luke 11:37-54)
5. Warnings to the people (Luke 12:1—13:9)
6. Healing in a synagogue (Luke 13:10-21)
7. Feast of the Dedication (John 10:22-39)
8. Withdrawal (John 10:40-42)
9. Jesus and the Pharisees (Luke 13:22—14:24)
10. Challenge to the multitudes (Luke 14:25-35)

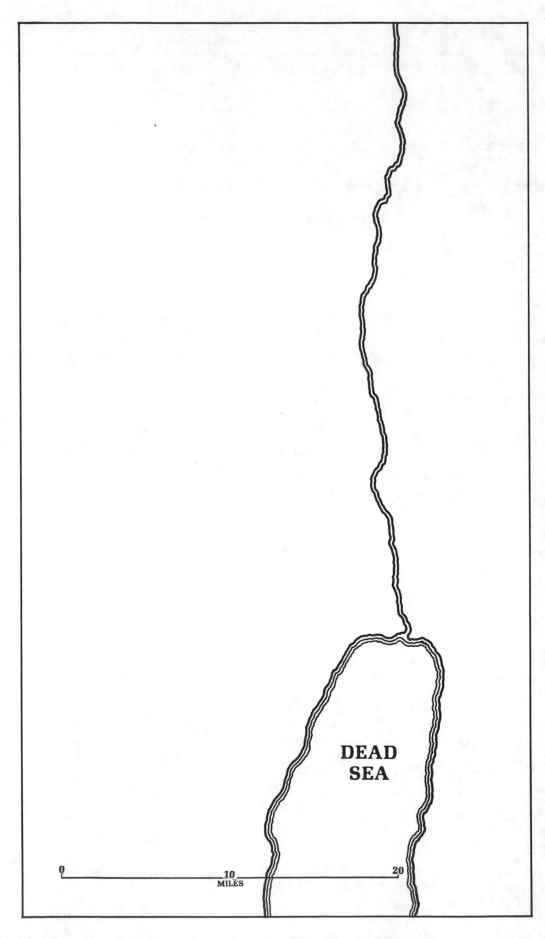

DEAD SEA

0   10   20
MILES

MINISTRY TO THE PEOPLE DESPITE OPPOSITION

And many nations will come and say, "Come and let us go up to the mountain of the Lord And to the house of the God of Jacob, That He may teach us about His ways And that we may walk in His paths." For from Zion will go forth the law, Even the word of the Lord from Jerusalem. MICAH 4:2

As Jesus traveled the Judean countryside, He taught about discipleship and dealt with false concepts the religious leaders were teaching. The Pharisees continued to challenge Him and tried to expose Him as an impostor.

MATTHEW 6:9-13   **LUKE 11:1-13**

Instructions on Prayer

Seeing Jesus habitually at prayer, the disciples asked Him to teach them how to pray, for they were conscious of their need for this relationship with the Father. So Jesus repeated His teaching on prayer, which focused Godward and manward.

1. Using the two focuses (Godward/manward) as your major divisions, outline and explain the Lord's Prayer in the chart below.

	OUTLINE	WHAT DOES IT MEAN?
G O D W A R D		
M A N W A R D		

2. How can the Lord's Prayer be used as a pattern for personal prayer?

_____

_____

_____

CROSS REFERENCES:
1 Thessalonians 5:17
1 Timothy 2:1
James 5:13-16

3. What reasons are given for persevering in prayer?

_____

_____

_____

Exposing the Religious Leaders

LUKE 11:14-54

Similar cures and similar teachings took place on different occasions in the ministry of Jesus. Partial repetition of the same teachings, as well as similar charges by His enemies, would be answered by substantially the same arguments Jesus had used before. The Pharisees probably brought the same charges many times to disrupt His work in a variety of locations. Once again when Jesus cast a demon out of a dumb man, the crowd marveled and certain leaders accused Him of doing so by the power of the devil (see Matthew 12:24). Other enemies again sought a sign from heaven under a pretext of piety.

4. Why was it impossible for Jesus to cast out demons by the power of Beelzebub?

_____

_____

5. How do the main points of these illustrations relate to Jesus?

STRONGMAN (11:21-22)

RETURNING UNCLEAN SPIRIT (11:24-26)

WOMAN BLESSING JESUS' MOTHER (11:27-28)

SIGN OF JONAH (11:29-30)

QUEEN OF THE SOUTH (11:31)
_____

SOLOMON (11:31)
_____

MEN OF NINEVEH (11:32)
_____

LAMP UNDER A BUSHEL (11:33)
_____

_____

EYE AS A LAMP (11:34-36)
_____

Jesus used the occasion of a dinner at the home of a Pharisee to expose a major sin. The act of ceremonial washing had become inordinately important to the Pharisees. This act had lost its purpose, and though everyone else probably practiced it Jesus noticeably did not.

6. What was one of the Pharisees' basic misconceptions? (11:38-41)

_____

_____

_____

7. What was the main point of each of the six woes that Jesus pronounced on the religious leaders? (11:42-52)

_____

_____

_____

_____

_____

_____

8. What are some of our modern-day practices that would bring forth woes by Jesus?

_____

_____

_____

**Warnings to
the People**

LUKE 12:1—13:21

"The consequence of the bold attack of Jesus on the whole system of Pharisaic and Scribal traditionalism was to precipitate great antagonism on the part of His enemies and draw about Him a vast throng of people (tens of thousands). Many of them were curiosity-mongers who desired to witness the debate between the discerning Rabbi [Jesus] and the keen lawyers, whose undying enmity He had incurred by His deliberate and daring denunciation of them. In the vast throng, there [probably] were many determined and enraged enemies, a considerable group of disciples, not a few sympathetic friends who had not yet become professed disciples, and many others, who were either indifferent or slightly prejudiced for or against Jesus.

"In the midst of these conditions of a varied assembly, Jesus wisely began His discourse, which would cover many topics according to the needs, by first addressing His disciple-group primarily, but in the presence of the vast multitude, so vast that they trampled on one another to get close enough to hear the speaker."[1]

9. Complete the chart below. This will help you identify and understand these warnings.

REFERENCE/ TO WHOM GIVEN	WARNING	WHAT THEY WERE TO DO
12:1-3		
12:4-7		
12:8-12		

1. J. W. Shepard, *The Christ of the Gospels* (Grand Rapids, Michigan: William B. Eerdmans Publishing Company, 1939), page 387.

REFERENCE/ TO WHOM GIVEN	WARNING	WHAT THEY WERE TO DO
12:13-21		
12:22-31		
12:32-34		
12:35-48		
12:49-53		
12:54-59		
13:1-9		
13:10-17		

10. How do the illustrations of the mustard seed and leaven relate to Jesus' warnings? (13:18-21)

_____

_____

_____

_____

_____

Feast of the Dedication

JOHN 10:22-42

The Feast of the Dedication was not biblical in origin. It was begun in 164 B.C. by Judas Maccabeus, a Jewish patriot who led his people to victory over the Syrians who controlled Palestine at the time. Antiochus Epiphanes, the ruler of Syria from 175 to 164 B.C., hated the Jews and had desecrated the temple some six years earlier. On winning their independence from the Syrians, the Jews celebrated by rededicating and purifying the temple at this feast. "The feast took place in December, toward the end of the month, and would thus be about three months later than the Feast of Tabernacles mentioned in [John] 7:2."[2]

11. What reasons did Jesus give for the people to believe that He was the Christ?

_____

_____

_____

12. What promises did He make to those who do believe?

_____

_____

_____

13. Why did some of the Jews try to stone Him?

_____

_____

_____

2. Merrill C. Tenney, *John: The Gospel of Belief* (Grand Rapids, Michigan: William B. Eerdmans Publishing Company, 1948), page 166.

LUKE 13:22—14:24

Jesus and the Pharisees

Jesus spoke boldly to His disciples and a great crowd of people, again cutting across the Jewish tradition system. His primary goal before this mixed audience was to address His disciples on the topic of hypocrisy. He had warned them against the corrupt teachings and examples of the Sadducees, Pharisees, and Herodians earlier in His ministry. Now He showed the foolishness of such living.

14. When asked if few would be saved, what did Jesus bring out in His answer? (13:22-30)

_____

_____

_____

Pretending concern for Jesus, the Pharisees warned Him of Herod Antipas' intention to kill Him. (Herod Antipas was the son of Herod the Great, who had ordered all male children in Bethlehem murdered. Like his father, he was superstitious, cunning, and totally immoral. After Christ's death, he was stripped of his power by Caesar Caius Caligula and banished to France, where he died in exile.)

15. How did Jesus answer this warning? (13:31-35)

_____

_____

_____

16. Why was Jesus determined to go to Jerusalem? (13:31-35)

_____

_____

_____

17. What did Jesus teach about the Sabbath? (14:1-6; see also Book I, Chapter 5)

_____

_____

_____

18. How can this teaching about the Sabbath be applied today?

_____

_____

_____

19. While in the Pharisee's home, Jesus taught three subjects. As you study LUKE 14, fill in the chart below.

REFERENCE/ WHAT STIMULATED JESUS TO SPEAK?	WHAT WAS HIS MAIN POINT?	WHAT RESPONSE DOES HE CALL FOR?
14:7–11		
14:12–14		
14:15–24		

Challenging the Multitudes

LUKE 14:25–35

With large crowds trailing behind Him, Jesus traveled toward Jerusalem and His impending death. Earlier in His ministry (Matthew 10:37–39) in Galilee, He had taught about discipleship. But now He spelled out the conditions for being a true disciple. He wanted His followers to think hard about the cost of following Him because He did not want them to be half-hearted. He knew that their enthusiasm would soon evaporate as He faced the cross instead of the presumed throne of Jewish expectations. (In this passage, the oriental term for hate expresses choosing one over against another or prizing more dearly.)

20. What prerequisites did Jesus set for those who would be His disciples?

PREREQUISITES	MEANING FOR TODAY

21. Why did He set such stringent requirements?

_____

_____

_____

_____

22. Review the chapter and your *Personal Notes* column, looking for a principle or truth you feel God wants you to apply in your life. Write out the application and any specific steps you intend to take:

_____

_____

_____

_____

_____

_____

_____

_____

Alexander, David and Patricia (eds.). *Eerdmans Handbook of the Bible.* Grand Rapids, Michigan: William B. Eerdmans Publishing Company, 1973.

Baxter, J. Sidlow. *Explore the Book.* Volume V. Grand Rapids, Michigan: Zondervan Publishing House, 1960.

Bruce, Alexander Balmain. *The Training of the Twelve.* New York: Doubleday & Company, Inc., 1928.

Daniel-Rops, Henri. *Daily Life in the Time of Jesus.* New York: Hawthorn Books, 1962.

Edersheim, Alfred. *The Life and Times of Jesus the Messiah.* Two Volumes. Grand Rapids, Michigan: William B. Eerdmans Publishing Company, n.d.

Geldenhuys, Norval. *Commentary on the Gospel of Luke.* Grand Rapids, Michigan: William B. Eerdmans Publishing Company, 1951.

Gundry, Robert H. *A Survey of the New Testament.* Grand Rapids, Michigan: Zondervan Publishing House, 1970.

Guthrie, Donald. *Jesus the Messiah.* Grand Rapids, Michigan: Zondervan Publishing House, 1972.

Hendriksen, William. *New Testament Commentary: The Gospel of Matthew.* Grand Rapids, Michigan: Baker Book House, 1973.

Marshall, I. H. "The Gospel According to Luke," *The New Bible Commentary Revised.* Grand Rapids, Michigan: William B. Eerdmans Publishing Company, 1970.

McNicol, J. "The Gospel According to Luke," *The New Bible Commentary.* Grand Rapids, Michigan: William B. Eerdmans Publishing Company, 1965.

Mears, Henrietta C. *What the Bible is All About.* Glendale, California: Gospel Light Publications, 1966.

Metzger, Bruce M. *The New Testament, Its Background, Growth, and Content.* New York: Abingdon Press, 1965.

Morgan, G. Campbell. *The Crises of the Christ.* Old Tappan, New Jersey: Fleming H. Revell Company, 1903.

National Geographic Society, *Everyday Life in Bible Times.* Washington, D.C.: National Geographic Society, 1967.

Orr, James (ed.). *The International Standard Bible Encyclopedia.* Five Volumes. Grand Rapids, Michigan: William B. Eerdmans Publishing Company, 1956.

Pink, Arthur W. *An Exposition of the Sermon on the Mount.* Swengel, Pennsylvania: Bible Truth Depot, 1950.

Robertson, A. T. *A Harmony of the Gospels.* New York: Harper & Brothers Publishers, 1950.

Sauer, Erich. *The Dawn of World Redemption.* Grand Rapids, Michigan: William B. Eerdmans Publishing Company, 1951.

Schaeffer, Francis and Edith. *Everybody Can Know.* Wheaton, Illinois: Tyndale House Publishers, 1974.

Scroggie, W. Graham. *A Guide to the Gospels.* Old Tappan, New Jersey: Fleming H. Revell Company, n.d.

Shepard, J. W. *The Christ of the Gospels.* Grand Rapids, Michigan: William B. Eerdmans Publishing Company, 1939.

Smith, David. *The Days of His Flesh.* New York: Harper & Brothers Publishers, n.d.

Stalker, James. *Life of Christ.* Old Tappan, New Jersey: Fleming H. Revell Company, 1909.

Stewart, James S. *The Life and Teaching of Jesus Christ.* Edinburgh: The Committee on Publications, the Church of Scotland, 1933.

Tasker, R.V.G. *The Gospel According to St. Matthew—An Introduction and Commentary.* Grand Rapids, Michigan: William B. Eerdmans Publishing Company, 1961.

Tenney, Merrill C. *John: The Gospel of Belief.* Grand Rapids, Michigan: William
    B. Eerdmans Publishing Company, 1948.
Tenney, Merrill C. *New Testament Times.* Grand Rapids, Michigan: William
    B. Eerdmans Publishing Company, 1965.
Unger, Merrill F. *Unger's Bible Handbook.* Chicago: Moody Press, 1966.

82   CHART OF THE LIFE AND MINISTRY OF JESUS CHRIST

BOOK	CHAPTER	SECTION	MATTHEW	MARK	LUKE	JOHN
I	ONE The Background to Christ's Coming	The Messiah's Coming Foretold				
		The Threefold Office of the Messiah				
		The Deity of the Messiah				1:1–18
		The Ancestry of the Messiah	1:1–17		3:23b–38	
		The Geographic Setting				
		The Men Who Wrote the Gospels		1:1	1:1–4	
		Two Promises				
		The Promise to Zacharias and Elizabeth			1:5–25	
		The Promise to Mary			1:26–38	
		Mary Visits Elizabeth			1:39–56	
		John's Birth			1:57–80	
Census ca. 5 B.C. Bethlehem	TWO Jesus' Birth and Childhood	Mary and Joseph	1:18–25			
		Jesus' Birth			2:1–20	
		Jesus Infancy				
		Presentation at the Temple			2:21–39a	
		Visit of the Wise Men	2:1–12			
Passover ca. A.D. 7 LUKE 2:41 Jerusalem		Flight into Egypt	2:13–23			
		Jesus' Youth			2:39b–52	
	THREE Preparation for Jesus' Ministry	John the Baptist	3:1–12	1:2–8	3:1–20	1:19–28
		Baptism of Jesus	3:13–17	1:9–11	3:21–23a	1:29–34
		Temptation in the Wilderness	4:1–11	1:12–13	4:1–13	
		Jesus' Early Followers				1:35–51
		Wedding at Cana				2:1–12
Passover ca. A.D. 27 JOHN 2:13 Jerusalem	FOUR Jesus' Manifestation to Israel	First Cleansing of the Temple				2:13–25
		Discussion with Nicodemus				3:1–21
		John the Baptist's Explanation of Jesus				3:22–36
		Conversion of the Samaritan Woman				4:1–42
	FIVE Authentication of Jesus' Mission by Healing	The Geographic Setting in Galilee	4:12	1:14–15	4:14–15	4:43–45
		Healing the Nobleman's Son				4:46–54
		Rejection at Nazareth			4:16–30	
		Move to Capernaum	4:13–17		4:31a	
		Gathering Disciples				
		The Fishermen	4:18–22	1:16–20	5:1–11	
		The Tax Collector	9:9–13	2:14–17	5:27–32	
		Healing and Teaching Ministry	8:2–4 14–17 9:1–8	1:21—2:13	4:31b–44 5:12–26	
		Discussion of Fasting with John's Disciples	9:14–17	2:18–22	5:33–39	
Passover ca. A.D. 28 JOHN 5:1 Jerusalem		The Sabbath Controversies	12:1–21	2:23—3:12	6:1–11	5:1–47
		Choosing the Twelve Apostles	10:2–4	3:13–19a	6:12–16	
	SIX The Sermon on the Mount	The Beatitudes	5:1–16		6:17–26	
		The True Meaning of the Law	5:17–48		6:27–36	
		Motives and Principles of Conduct	6:1–8 6:14—7:12		6:37–42	
		Exhortations and Commands	7:13—8:1		6:43–49	

BOOK	CHAPTER	SECTION	MATTHEW	MARK	LUKE	JOHN
II	**ONE** **Opposition to** **Jesus' Ministry**	Healing the Centurion's Servant	8:5–13		7:1–10	
		Raising a Widow's Son			7:11–17	
		Reassuring John the Baptist	11:2–30		7:18–35	
		Anointing by a Sinful Woman			7:36—8:3	
		Dealing with False Accusations	12:22–45	3:19b–30		
		Jesus' Family Seeks Him	12:46–50	3:31–35	8:19–21	
		Teaching by Parables	13:1–53	4:1–34	8:4–18	
		Stilling a Tempest	8:23–27	4:35–41	8:22–25	
	TWO **Expansion of** **Jesus' Ministry**	Curing a Demoniac	8:28–34	5:1–20	8:26–39	
		Raising Jairus' Daughter	9:18–35	5:21–43	8:40–56	
		Nazareth's Second Rejection of Jesus	13:54–58	6:1–6		
		Sending out the Twelve	9:36—11:1	6:7–13	9:1–6	
		Death of John the Baptist	14:1–12	6:14–29	9:7–9	
		Feeding the Five Thousand	14:13–21	6:30–44	9:10–17	6:1–13
		Jesus Walks on Water	14:22–36	6:45–56		6:14–21
		Discourse on the Bread of Life				6:22–71
	THREE **Further Clashes** **with the** **Pharisees**	Exposing Hypocrisy	15:1–20	7:1–23		7:1
		Healing the Canaanite Woman's Daughter	15:21–28	7:24–30		
		Feeding the Four Thousand	15:29–39	7:31—8:10		
		The Leaven of the Pharisees	16:1–12	8:11–21		
		Healing a Blind Man		8:22–26		
	FOUR **A New** **Direction**	Peter's Great Confession	16:13–20	8:27–30	9:18–21	
		Jesus Foretells His Death and Resurrection	16:21–28	8:31—9:1	9:22–27	
		The Transfiguration	17:1–13	9:2–13	9:28–36	
		Healing a Demon-possessed Boy	17:14–21	9:14–29	9:37–43a	
		Return to Capernaum	17:22–23	9:30–32	9:43b–45	
		Paying the Temple Tax	17:24–27			
		A Discourse by Jesus	18:1–35	9:33–50	9:46–50	
		Traveling to Jerusalem	8:18–22 19:1–2	10:1	9:51–62	7:2–10
	FIVE **Encounters in** **Jerusalem**	Discourse on Living Water				7:11–53
		Mercy for an Adulteress				8:1–11
		Jesus' Teaching about Himself				8:12–59
		Healing a Blind Man				9:1–41
		Discourse on the Good Shepherd				10:1–21
		Seventy New Laborers			10:1–24	
		The Good Neighbor			10:25–37	
		Visiting Mary and Martha			10:38–42	
	SIX **Ministry to the** **People Despite** **Opposition**	Instructions on Prayer	6:9–13		11:1–13	
		Exposing the Religious Leaders			11:14–54	
		Warnings to the People			12:1—13:21	
		Feast of the Dedication				10:22–42
		Jesus and the Pharisees			13:22—14:24	
		Challenging the Multitudes			14:25–35	

Passover
ca. A.D. 29
JOHN 6:4
Jerusalem

BOOK	CHAPTER	SECTION	MATTHEW	MARK	LUKE	JOHN
III	**ONE** **Jesus' Teachings** **in Light of** **Rejection**	Three Parables			15:1–32	
		Teaching His Disciples			16:1—17:10	
		Raising Lazarus from the Dead				11:1–54
		Healing the Lepers			17:11–19	
		The Messianic Kingdom			17:20–37	
		Two Parables on Prayer			18:1–14	
		Marriage and Divorce	19:3–12	10:2–12		
		Jesus and the Children	19:13–15	10:13–16	18:15–17	
		The Rich Young Ruler	19:16—20:16	10:17–31	18:18–30	
		Rebuking James and John	20:17–28	10:32–45	18:31–34	
	TWO **Jesus'** **Triumphal** **Entry into** **Jerusalem**	Events at Jericho				
		Healing Bartimaeus	20:29–34	10:46–52	18:35–43	
		Ministering to Zaccheus			19:1–10	
		Parable of the Pounds			19:11–28	
		Arrival in Bethany				11:55—12:1 12:9–11
		The Triumphal Entry	21:1–11 14–17	11:1–11	19:29–44	12:12–19
		Symbolic Events				
		Cursing the Fig Tree	21:18–19a	11:12–14		
		Second Cleansing of the Temple	21:12–13	11:15–19	19:45–48	
		The Visit of the Greeks				12:20–50
		A Long Day				
		The Withered Fig Tree	21:19b–22	11:20–26		
		The Question of Jesus' Authority	21:23–27	11:27–33	20:1–8	
		Three Parables of Warning	21:28—22:14	12:1–12	20:9–19	
		Three Questions	22:15–40	12:13–34	20:20–40	
		Jesus' Question	22:41–46	12:35–37	20:41–44	
	THREE **Continued** **Encounters** **and Teachings**	Warning to the Disciples	23:1–12	12:38–40	20:45–47	
		Denunciation of the Pharisees	23:13–39			
		The Widow's Two Copper Coins		12:41–44	21:1–4	
		The Mount Olivet Discourse	24:1—25:46	13:1–37	21:5–36	
		Predictions of the Crucifixion	26:1–5	14:1–2	22:1–2	
		Anointing Jesus for Burial	26:6–13	14:3–9		12:2–8
		Secret Meeting of Judas and the Leaders	26:14–16	14:10–11	22:3–6	
Passover *ca.* A.D. 30 JOHN 13:1 Jerusalem	**FOUR** **Final** **Instructions** **to the Disciples**	Preparation for the Last Supper	26:17–19	14:12–16	22:7–13	
		Partaking of the Passover	26:20	14:17	22:14–16 24–30	
		Washing the Disciples' Feet				13:1–20
		Betrayal Foretold	26:21–25	14:18–21	22:21–23	13:21–30
		Institution of the Lord's Supper	26:26–29	14:22–25	22:17–20	13:31–35
		Discussion on Where Jesus Was Going	26:30	14:26		13:36—14:31
		Discourse on Bearing Fruit				15:1–27
		Revealing the Future				16:1–33
		The Great High Priestly Prayer				17:1–26
		Peter's Denial Predicted	26:31–35	14:27–31	22:31–38	
	FIVE **Jesus' Sufferings** **on Behalf of Men**	The Agony of Gethsemane	26:36–46	14:32–42	22:39–46	18:1
		The Betrayal	26:47–56	14:43–52	22:47–54a	18:2–12
		The Jewish Trials	26:57 59–68 27:1	14:53 55–65 15:1a	22:54b 63–71	18:13–14 19–24
		Peter's Denial	26:58 69–75	14:54 66–72	22:54c–62	18:15–18 25–27
		Judas' Suicide	27:3–10			ACTS 1:18–19
		The Roman Trials	27:2 11–31a	15:1b–20a	23:1–25	18:28—19:16a
		The Crucifixion	27:31b–56	15:20b–41	23:26–49	19:16b–37
		The Burial	27:57–66	15:42–47	23:50–56	19:38–42

BOOK	CHAPTER	SECTION	MATTHEW	MARK	LUKE	JOHN
III	**SIX** **Jesus'** **Victory and** **Commission**	The Resurrection and First Appearances	28:1–15	16:1–11	24:1–12	20:1–18
		Appearance on the Road to Emmaus		16:12	24:13–33a	
		Appearances to Peter and the Apostles		16:13–14	24:33b–43	20:19–25
		Appearance to Convince Thomas				20:26–31
		Appearance by the Sea of Galilee				21:1–25
		The Great Commission	28:16–20	16:15–18		
		The Commission Repeated			24:44–49	ACTS 1:3–8
		The Ascension		16:19–20	24:50–53	ACTS 1:9–12

THE LIFE

and ministry of Jesus Christ clearly shows the purpose for which He came into this world—to bring sinful men back to God. The practical application of that great truth for a person who has never trusted Jesus Christ as Saviour and Lord is to receive Him into his or her life.

The following is a simple Gospel presentation, useful for Christians to share with others. It also shows the way to Jesus Christ, whose life and ministry you have just studied, if you have never received Him as your own Saviour and Lord.

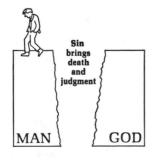

The Bible teaches that God loves all men and wants them to know Him.

But man is separated from God and His love.
"God is on one side and all the people on the other side."
1 Timothy 2:5, Living Bible

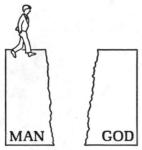

Why is man separated from God and His love?

Because he has sinned against God.
"Your iniquities have made a separation between you and your God."
Isaiah 59:2
"For all have sinned and fall short of the glory of God."
Romans 3:23

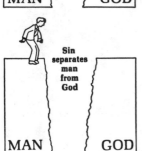

Where does this separation lead?

This separation leads only to death and certain judgment.
"Man is destined to die once, and after that to face judgment."
Hebrews 9:27
"Those who do not know God . . . will be punished with everlasting destruction and shut out from the presence of the Lord."
2 Thessalonians 1:8-9

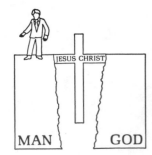

<u>But</u>, there is a solution.

Jesus Christ, who died on the cross for our sins, is the way to God.
"God is on one side and all the people on the other side, and Christ Jesus, Himself man, is between them to bring them together, by giving His life for all mankind."
1 Timothy 2:5, Living Bible

"Christ died for sins once for all . . . to bring you to God."

Does this include everyone?

No. Only those who personally receive Jesus Christ into their lives, trusting Him to forgive their sins.
"Yet to all who received Him, to those who believed in His name, He gave the right to become children of God."
John 1:12

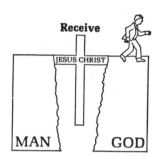

Each one must decide for himself whether to receive Christ.

Jesus says, "Here I am! I stand at the door and knock. If anyone hears My voice and opens the door, I will go in and eat with him, and he with Me."
Revelation 3:20

How does a person receive Jesus Christ?

Jesus said, "You may ask Me for anything in My name, and I will do it."
John 14:14

Therefore if you pray sincerely, asking Him—
> *Lord Jesus, please come into my life*
> *and be my Saviour and Lord*
> *Please forgive my sins,*
> *And give me the gift of eternal life*
> **—He will do it now.**

If you have invited Jesus Christ into your life, the Bible says you now have eternal life.

"And this is the testimony: God has given us eternal life, and this life is in His Son. He who has the Son has life; he who does not have the Son of God does not have life."
1 John 5:11-12

This book is part of a three-book series on *The Life and Ministry of Jesus Christ*. You should have all three books if you are to get a complete picture of the person and work of the Saviour. The other books are available from your local Christian bookstore.